Acknowledgements

My thanks go firstly to John Melloy for his work on the text of the original book Others who have assisted,
with photographs or other material, are the late Charles Cawood, Bob Moorhouse, Graham Edwards, Stephen
Moate, and Perkins Engines.v

The Nuffield Tractor Story

The Nuffield Organisation was the umbrella title for the group of Companies associated with Morris Motors Ltd. William Morris, later Lord Nuffield had set up Morris Motors Ltd. in 1913 and in addition to the range of popular family cars developed over the years a range of commercial vehicles and even buses were offered. There were moves towards involvement in tractors on several occasions, notably work with Roadless Traction in the 1920s and an abortive attempt to get Morris Motors involved in tractors by Harry Ferguson in 1930 which was stalled by Morris due to the onslaught of the recession.

The Second World War saw involvement in tank and crawler vehicle production and like so many Motor Manufacturers finished the war with excess capacity. Britain had built up an enormous trade deficit with the United States as a result of 'lend lease' and the Government placed exports at a premium with what materials were available. The War had a considerable impact on farm mechanisation and it was expected that demand for tractors in the 1946-50 period would be at an all-time high. Although Fordson production had been 'topped up' with US imports from 1939-45 the way ahead was, in an ideal world, to be able to supply all tractors for the UK market from UK industry and use the extra capacity to expand in export markets. In fact it was the overseas potential which was given priority from the start and British Farmers still had to wait for their 'new' machine, even requiring a WAC permit until 1949 to allow purchase of same.

'NUFFIELD TO MAKE TRACTORS" was the announcement made by Sir Miles Thomas, vice-chairman of the Nuffield Organisation when he spoke to the I.S.M.A. at Hull in late March 1946. The tractor would have been 30% more power and be 30% sturdier than the average tractor available due to the involvement in its design by Mr Claude Culpin and Dr H. E. Merritt, who was well known for his part in tank design during the war.

The tractor was to be called the Nuffield Universal and was intended to be an all round farm machine with a high level of specification and fitments. Within two months the first prototype tractor was being field tested in Lincolnshire and by the end of the summer another dozen machines were being used for performance reports prior to a demonstration of three and four wheeled tractors at Pershore in late 1946. The prototype tractor bore a considerable resemblance to David Brown designs; indeed it is said that the David Brown 50D was under development when Dr. Merritt moved to the Nuffield Organisation and therefore both tractors come from the same lineage.

It was fully intended to proceed with production in a big way in 1947, but due to material shortages this was not possible. However, the design team was kept hard at work improving the tractor and fitments, this included a completely new hydraulic lift.

By 1948 materials became available to the Nuffield Organisation to start tractor production with a stipulation by the Government that the first 12 months production be sold in the UK market to help produce home~grown foodstuffs after the war years.

Introduced at the Smithfield Show, in December 1948, the new 'Nuffield Universal' production models were a deal bigger than the prototypes and also sported revised tinwork and the new hydraulic lift, built at the old Wolseley factory in Birmingham. The tractors were painted poppy orange, and black engine accessories; priced at £487 for the basic M3 (three wheeler) and £495 for the M4 (four wheeler).

Listed as extras were the hydraulic lift and PTO unit at £60, belt pulley £12, and electric lights £9.

The tractors used a Morris Commercial ETA (M4) and ETB (IM4) four cylinder side valve engine (which had been originally designed for army use). Running on vaporising oil, the HP developed at 2000rpm was 38. The manifold was fitted with a heat shield and incorporated an adjustable hot spot operated by an external control; a lever operated radiator shutter gave accurate temperature control and the fuel system had independent cocks and sediment bowls.

By late 1950 the 2000th Nuffield Universal tractor had been exported by Nuffield Exports Ltd., to such countries as: Australia, New Zealand, Sweden, Holland, Denmark, Eire and Egypt; a shipment was due to go to Argentina early in 1951 and it was expected that an order would be despatched to the Belgian Congo which would be an entirely new market for British tractors.

1950 saw the introduction of the diesel engined Nuffield tractor which used the proven Perkins P4; this model was bought out to extend the range to three models available in three or four wheel form priced at £490 for a basic M4 to £667.10s0d (£667.50) for the high specification DM4. Standard equipment included electric starting, canvas cover and swinging, adjustable drawbar. Optional equipment included hydraulic power unit, belt pulley, electric lighting, wheel weights, etc.

In 1952 the British Motor Corporation was formed by the merger of Austin and Morris, and the tractors were produced by Morris Motors Ltd., Agricultural Division, Birmingham. A redesigned engine 'ETC' which raised the bhp to 43 was introduced in March / April 1953. This had improved combustion chambers, the cylinder head had long reach 14mm plugs, and ignition was by coil and distributor; the engine lubrication system was also improved and by moving the starting dog to the snout of the crankshaft the starting handle could be used even if the front end weight was fitted. Other changes in the model at this time were the fitting of a mid-mounted drawbar, hand clutch and overload release, and the replacement of the single front wheel by two wheels mounted close together on the steering pillar and sharply cambered, the tractor serial numbers with these changes started at 11954 (M4) and 75860 (PM4) but the basic price remained unchanged at £465 for the M4.

By March 1954, a new diesel engine designed and manufactured by BMC was available and Nuffield tractors with this unit were first seen at the Royal Highland Show in June. The OEA2 engine was a four cylinder direct injection type with bore and stroke of 95mm and 120mm respectively; capacity was 3402cc and it was claimed to be 10% more economical on fuel than the P4 that it replaced. Power at the flywheel was 45bhp, other features were the five bearing counter-balanced crankshaft, replaceable wet cylinder liners, Lucas 12-volt starting equipment and Simms fuel injection. Induction and exhaust manifolds were mounted on opposite sides of the engine with air cleaner pre-deaner mounted under the bonnet. These tractors were also called model DM and the price for the basic model remained at £597.10s0d (£597.50), ex works.

Also in 1954, the hydraulic lift pump was increased from 1000psi to 2000psi working pressure. The serial number position for the hydraulic power unit was stamped on the cross shaft housing next to the valve adjusting screws, and the early units which had BSF type threads ended at no. 17979. This was superceded by the unit using unified threads at no. 17980 and the new 2000lbs unit began at 2000 IUOO1. Further improvements to the DM were the fitting of an improved oil filler which extended through the bonnet top, an independent PTO which was listed as an additional extra on new tractors only.

In 1957 a smaller tractor was added to the range, the Universal Three which used a 3 cylinder version of the 3.4 litre BMC diesel. It was a bit cumbersome compared with other models at the lower end of the market and did not become as popular as equivalent Ford or MF models. The DM4 became the Universal Four at the same time and the only outward change in appearance was the lack of sliding rear hubs which up until then had been a standard fitting. By 1957/58 the PM series tractors were only produced for export and the M4 was slowly being phased out due to the popularity of the diesel engine.

Production was then moved to the Morris factory at Cowley, near Oxford; consequently two new tractors were announced in November 1961 in time for the Royal Smithfield Show as the Nuffield 3/42 and 4/60. The 4/60 used a BMC 3.8 litre engine, producing 60bhp at 2000 rpm, but still retained the five speed gearbox of the original DM4 series, whilst most competitors were offering a dual range 6-forward and 2-reverse transmission.

Another factory move was made in 1963, this time to Bathgate, in Scotland, where a new £11 1/4 million automatic assembly plant had been built and both engines and transmissions were made there along with BMC trucks. The following year both models were revised again, to become the 10/42 and the 10/60, so called because they now offered 10 forward and 2 reverse gears.

These two tractors were also fitted with an improved independent dual-flow hydraulic system, disc brakes and twin headlamps. Both tractors were offered in either basic, standard, or deluxe form, and a range of optional equipment was available.

In 1965 BMC announced their new lightweight Mini Tractor as a new era in power farn-ting 'n-iini mechanisation'. Designed to be used round the farms for smaller jobs it used a 950cc diesel engine, nine forward and reverse motion. This small tractor had its ancestry in the TE Ferguson, indeed the tractor was developed on behalf of BMC by Harry Ferguson Research Ltd. of Coventry, and had the hydraulic power unit mounted above the engine, and the oil tank was located under the driving seat for easy refuelling. Colour scheme was Nuffield orange, with white wheels and grille panel.

The last of the Nuffield range was introduced in 1967 at the Royal Show as the 3 45 and 4/65 models, available to basic, standard or deluxe specifications. Designed with the driver's needs in mind, the 3 45 and 4 /65 models had an extended mainframe to carry the 15 gallon fuel tank forward ,of the engine ; wide mudwings and footplates were also fitted along with a comprehensive range of instruments housed in a weatherproof panel. For easy access the engine cover

could be raised without having to remove the exhaust pipe and for the first time ever, a Nuffield tractor was fitted with radius rods as standard.

Mechanically, these tractors were very much the same as the ones they had replaced, with a 3770cc four cylinder engine in the 4/65 and a 2827cc three cylinder in the 3/45. In November 1968 the 'mini tractor' was updated and fitted with a larger 1489cc engine and was known as the 4/25.

In 1968 BMC were taken over by Leyland and at the Royal Show that year, Lord Stokes, chairman of BLMC announced that the Nuffield tractor would be retained and developed under his re-organisation of BLMC. A new design team was set up at Bathgate to work on the tractor project and a year later the new models were announced as the 'Blue Range of Leyland'.

Sadly, after nearly a quarter of a century, the Nuffield name was dropped in favour of the famous truck and bus 'Leyland' badge, and the orange and white colour scheme gave way to two-tone blue, and silver on the new 384, 344 and 154 models. These new tractors did not change much from the Nuffields they replaced, apart from styling, and the 344 used a four cylinder-3402cc engine instead of a three cylinder type in the 3/45. The 154 was identical to the 4 /25 and a petrol engine was available as an option.

From 1970 the Leyland tractor range was increased in many ways and improvements to such items as cabs, hydraulics, four wheel drive and turbo charged engines, and by December 1980 they had a range of 10 models on offer. December 1980 saw the introduction of a new range of models and a new yellow /black colour scheme on the 2 and 4 wheel drive tractors, but the 285 and 2100 models were dropped.

The late 1970s found many problems for BLMC, not least the desire of the New Thatcher Government to relieve the taxpayer of the burden of BLMC's mounting losses. Add to this the poor quality control record at Bathgate which even went back to the early 1970s, with dealers at one time having to claim warranty work on over 80% of production, and the future looked bleak for Leyland's Tractor division.

In 1981, Charles Nickerson, who owned Track Marshall, floated a company to purchase the Leyland wheeled tractor division from Bathgate and proceeded to move all production machinery and stock to Gainsborough, where the tractors were to be produced by a new company: Marshall Sons & Company Ltd., when the tractors appeared under the slogan 'made better by Marshall', the specification remained the same as the previous models, but the Marshall formula was used to make existing features even better. Smithfield 1982 saw the name Marshall in place of Leyland, but the model numbers remained unchanged with tractors ranging from 30 to 80 bhp.

By 1983 Marshall were obviously losing out on the higher horsepower market, so, using German ZF transmissions, 100 and 115HP tractors were added to the range, using Leyland engines. It had been hoped to move production of Leyland tractor engines to Gainsborough.

Prospects looked good for Marshall, but, in 1985 the company went into receivership. The track Marshall concern stayed put in a part of the works at Gainsborough following a management buyout, whilst the wheeled tractor side passed to Bentall Simplex, who moved stocks to Scunthorpe. A small number of tractors were assembled using Perkins engines and other bought in components but the Nuffield tractor which is the subject of this book had really passed from the scene in its true sense.

Left: An artist's impression of the Nuffield Universal Tractor. This drawing was used for advance publicity once it had been decided to put the tractor into production. Note the remarkable similarity to a David Brown at this stage, including the bench type seat. How one started the tractor is a mystery as certain details such as the aperture for a starting handle have been omitted from the impression.

Below: Prototype tractors were tested in July 1946 and this shows what the three wheeled model looked like at the gestation stage. Invited guests were shown the tractor at a demonstration at Pershore and these included representatives from the Ministry of Agriculture, the Press, and leading figures from the farming industry.

Bottom: A thorough testing programme using the prototypes was embarked upon under all types of conditions found on British farms. This illustration was taken near Spalding in Lincolnshire. Note the fuel filler to the left side of the bonnet and the starting handle location.

Above: The same tractor as in the previous picture from the other side. No hydraulics were fitted at this stage. However, once the development boys at Nuffield became aware of the impending introduction of such items on the Fordson Major, and the launch of the Fergie 20 in the UK, no time was lost in adding this feature.

Below: This four wheeler is now reaching an appearance closely resembling the production tractors. The bonnet details have, however, not been finalised, although the front grille is now almost to production standards. The fuel system for the automatic changeover from petrol to TVO can be clearly seen.

Above: One of the prototypes on test at the NIAE at Silsoe, Beds, during 1946.   The dynamometer car attached to the drawbar is equipped to measure drawbar pull, fuel consumption, and thus calculate drawbar horsepower.   Tests on the prototypes were usually unpublished, a standard tractor being sent from the production line, when in operation, for the published tests.   At this stage the toolbox was mounted on top of the frame on the right side of the engine.

Below: Taken at an unknown location, this view shows the first design of hydraulic lift.   A considerable amount of development work was to take place before the final version went into production.   At one stage an alternative hand lift was considered.   It is possible that the trial version of this came from a proprietary source such as Stanhays.

Right: Looking down on an early production M4 tractor with bonnet removed. The large radiator cap on early production is to be noted, as is the central position of the fuel filler cap. The steering wheel remains offset however.

Below: The Morris foundry in Coventry with rough gearbox and frame castings for Nuffield tractors being collected for despatch to the Drews lane plant for machining. Products from the competition are being used to facilitate this; A Fordson Major E27N with Chaseside 1 ton crane, and in the background an earlier model N loading shovel by Chaseside deals with coke and limestone for the cupolas and sand for moulding.

Testing a pre-production tractor at Coleshill.   The tinwork is almost to production standards and the toolbox has been moved to the rear of the tractor.

Another two views of a pre-production prototype on test at Coleshill in late 1947. Larger tyre sizes are evident along with modified wheel centres. The use of a three furrow plough might tax the tractor somewhat - two were more within its capacity.

Above: In the experimental shop of the Wolseley works at Drews Lane a production M4 tractor has been taken off the line and prepared for despatch to the 1948 Smithfield Show.   It was at this event in December 1948 that the general public first had sight of the tractor.

Below: A cutaway drawing of the Nuffield Universal M4 tractor showing the internal layout.

INTERCHANGEABLE FRONT AXLE
FOR NUFFIELD UNIVERSAL
THREE WHEELED TRACTOR

NUFFIE
UNIVER

Above: Interchangeability of components to enable the Nuffield to operate as a three or four wheel tractor was part of the original concept.   This posed shot shows both types of axle.

Right: One of the later prototypes showing the single front wheel. Note again the toolbox location. It is quite possible that this tractor GOL496 being one of the development prototypes was modified to bring it into line with production standards, or that the registration plate was used on various prototypes.

GOL 496

The experimental shop at Drews Lane again with tractors being readied for show use.   Badges and decals have yet to be affixed.

Above: The tractor seen in this photograph MJL949 was widely photographed in both three and four wheeled configurations for publicity use and the sales literature for the 1948-52 period made use of many of the photographs. The location was Lincolnshire, in the Spalding area.

Below: The early pattern ETA Morris M4 Petrol/TVO engine. Points to note are the dual fuel sediment bulbs, the special Carburettor to allow automatic changeover from petrol to TVO, and engine hourmeter attached to the timing train.

Above: Opportunity was taken at Agricultural shows to display the whole range of Morris products available to the agricultural industry as this shot of a Nuffield Universal M3 taken at the 1949 Bath & West Show also features a Morris J type bodied as a milk float. Whilst it was not usual for Morris Commercial and Nuffield to share a stand at the larger shows, where local dealers held franchises for both, County and local shows often saw the two product lines together.

Right: Following some concern over the stability of the single front wheel assembly Nuffield revised the layout to a vee twin formation as seen here.

Right: This rear view of an early production M4 tractor with drawbar attached using pins and cotters. Later production tractors had the drawbar bolted on. This is a basic specification tractor, with no hydraulics, but this could be retrofitted by a dealer.

Below. This 1950 PM4 not only shows the fuel system configuration for an all petrol tractor. As this is for an export customer in the Belgian Congo oversize tyres and twin headlamps are fitted. Until legislation required it, domestic deliveries only had one headlamp.

Below: Like other manufacturers, Nuffield had not developed its own diesel engine when market demand necessitated the introduction of a diesel model in 1950. Perkins supplied their P4 engine for this model which was designated DM4 in the case of the four wheeled example shown here on a Perkins stand at a 1950 event, and DM3 in the case of the tricycle version.

Right: The P4(TA) engine as fitted to the Nuffield. When tested by Silsoe the tractor gave a maximum belt horsepower of 36.7 and drawbar horsepower of 31.2. The rated engine speed was 2000 rpm. for belt work and 1400 rpm for field work. Perkins also marketed a conversion pack to enable earlier tractors to be converted to diesel.

Opposite page, above and below: Four pictures taken by Perkins official photographers of the Nuffield Universal tractor fitted with Perkins P4(TA) engine at work in the Peterborough area.   The cab is by Scottish Aviation

Certainly not common on the Nuffield were steel wheels, supplied by Sankey.   These were identical to the pattern supplied to Ford except for the centre fixings - even the front wheels show affinity to the Fordson on steel wheels.   The cab above is by Winsam and carries the appropriate 'approved implement' badge. The Howard Rotovator fitted in the illustration below required removal of the lower linkage to allow attachment.   Top gear was blanked on tractors supplied on steel wheels by means of a sleeve on the selector rail.

Above: The DM4 model with Perkins diesel required relocation of the air cleaner.   In this shot of a Huntingdonshire registered tractor the potato harvester is intended to be the main subject.

Below: Three wheeled diesels were rare, but this shot worked up by the publicity department was to be seen in many contemporary advertisements in the 1950-4 period.   The Perkins engine was used from March 1950 until March 1954.

The 1953 introduction of the Perkins L4 engine saw Perkins offer a conversion pack using this power unit to replace ETA and ETC Petrol and TVO engines in earlier Nuffield tractors. Some surgery to the bonnet was required to relocate the exhaust and air cleaner, and a modified battery housing was provided. The photos show a tractor at work in the Peterborough area.

Morris Motors and Austin became part of the British Motor Corporation in 1952. This allowed for the joint development of a diesel engine suitable for medium commercial and tractor use. It was produced in four and six cylinder forms and became the standard diesel engine in both Austin and Morris Commercial Vehicles as well as being used by other manufacturers such as Dennis and Guy. The end result was that in 1954 the 4DM Nuffield tractor which used the BMC OEA2 Diesel engine was announced.

Above: A tractor to export specification with oversize tyres, front weight attachment and rear wheel weights is seen at the NIAE at Silsoe.

Below: The official 1954 publicity photograph of the 4DM showing the BMC diesel badge on the front grille. A Perkins engine was still available for certain export territories however.

Above: The mainframe casting on the Nuffield was conveniently drilled to allow the attachment of such items as the Catchpole mid mounted toolbar seen here. Capable of taking attachments for different jobs, the toolbar was connected to the tractor lift by means of chains.

Below: This Nuffield Universal with Lambourn cab disguises the fact that it is one of the development tractors leading to the introduction of the 4/60. The standard Sankey rear wheel centres with six stud fixings give the game away.

Above: With other manufacturers moving towards a 'heavy and light' model policy Nuffield developed their smaller model over the period from 1955-1956 and launched the "Universal Three" in August 1957. One of the prototypes is seen ploughing near Birmingham in the summer of 1957.   The engine was simply the four cylinder unit redesigned with one less bore into a three cylinder one.

Below: A shot of the same tractor taken at the factory.   The family resemblance between the Universal Three and Universal Four models was more marked than that of other manufacturer's light and heavy models.

Above: The Universal Three was demonstrated to the Farming Press in August 1957. By now the badging had been approved. Sadly, this tractor did not come up to expectations in gaining sales from customers who were buying Ferguson 35s and Fordson Dextas.

Below: The BMC 2.55 litre 3 cylinder diesel as fitted to the Universal Three.

Above: An early production Universal Three at Drews Lane being photographed against a white sheet to allow the artists to produce publicity illustrations without a background.   Such illustrations were used in the drivers handbook and on Advertising material.

Below: Four wheel drive was under development by the experimental dept. at Drews Lane.   One of two known prototypes dating from 1960, based on a Universal Four, is seen here.

Above: The Nuffield Universal Three tractor showing some of the extras available including rear wheel weights, front weight attachment, seat cover and front and rear number plate mountings.

Below: With the introduction of the Universal Three, the four cylinder model was given the "Universal Four" name.   This photograph provides a good comparison between the two models; note that the sliding hubs of the earlier model have gone, being only available on the Universal Four to order.   The tall intake stack was a feature of some export models.

Above: Here an export model Universal Three with twin headlamps compares with a Universal Four for domestic sale with sliding rear hubs.

Below: The same two tractors from the rear shows that the rear axle configuration of both models shared many common components;   the only difference being in the rear wheel and tyre sizes and a reduced mudguard profile.

Above: Existing production tractors were used by the experimental dept. as development models.   What purports to be a Universal Four is in fact a prototype Nuffield 4/60 tractor seen in 1960.

Below: A genuine Universal Four appears in this 1959 posed shot which was issued to the press and appeared in most of the farming papers.

Photographs of tractors in their working environments were important for publicity purposes as even in the 1950s many smaller farms shunned mechanisation of certain tasks. In this muck shifting scene the Universal Four is fitted with a Horndraulic loader and a Winsam cab can be seen on the tractor in the background. Morris Motors Headquarters were in Oxford, hence the Oxfordshire registrations on the tractors.

A Nuffield Universal Four tractor from the Nuffield Tractor Training School seen ploughing in 1958/9. It was considered essential for dealer staff to be able to perform certain farming tasks competently either purely for demonstration purposes, or in the case of service staff, to understand the performance of the tractors in their working environments.

Above: *Lucas experimented with various alternative transmissions for tractors in the 1960s and converted this Nuffield 4/60 in 1962.   In place of a conventional gearbox, a torque converter gave an infinite speed range.   A similar unit was later fitted to skid units supplied to JCB.*

Below: *Looking north over the BMC factory at Bathgate with Grangemouth and the Ochil hills in the background.   The new plant, to which tractor production was transferred during 1962/3, was purpose built and also housed the BMC Bus and Truck division.   The series of single story buildings in the bottom right foreground were the tractor training school, known as Moss-side Farm after the steading of that name which once occupied the site of the plant.*

Above: The Nuffield 3/42 tractor was introduced in December 1961 and was an update of the Universal Three with engine power increased by 5HP to 42BHP. This artist's impression using a photograph of the Universal Three as a basis shows two headlights.

Opposite page above: At the time of its introduction in 1961 the Nuffield 4/60 developed 60BHP @ 2000rpm. and was therefore the most powerful British made tractor of its time.

Opposite page below: This tractor has been prepared for show display and is fitted with the optional extras of power steering and 14x30 rear wheels and tyres.

Below: The artist has on this occasion created the export model 3/42 with twin headlamps, oversize rear tyres, and exhaust and air intake stack extensions.

The 10/42 (above) and 10/60 (below) were announced in August 1964. The two models are seen here in export form with oversize tyres and air intake extensions.

Below: The equivalent small model was the 10/42 - note the BMC 'Drivers Club' badge on the grille.

Above: The 10/60 followed the trend in being fitted with disc brakes, a ten speed gearbox, and improved hydraulics. The first production tractors were retained for publicity use and received the JO (Oxfordshire) registrations as shown.

Working shots of the 10/60 (above) with Rotovator, and the 10/42 (below) ploughing.

Above: The Italian built Cantatore Field Boy, powered by a BMC 2.2 litre diesel engine, was produced by Vittorio Cantatore who also imported Nuffield tractors into Italy. In style and paint finish it hyped the Nuffield tractor. An example was imported and tested in the UK during 1957 but nothing further came of this.

Below: The BMB President tractor built in Southport by Brockhouse Engineering used a Morris side valve 16hp engine. It had a production run of nearly six years from 1950-1956. The Nuffield organisation tested the President in 1952 as part of its policy of testing its own power units as applied to other manufacturers products and due consideration was taken to acquire the production rights of the tractor. This was later abandoned when it was realised that other manufacturers were developing products that would be far superior. The example shown here is an orchard model.

Above: The BMC Mini tractor turning hay with a Vicon Acrobat.   The tractor is also equipped for attachment of a Mil front loader.

Below: The Nuffield family of tractors in 1965.   The Nuffield 10/60 (60HP), BMC Mini (16HP) and the Nuffield 10/42 (42HP).

Right: In the event BMC set about the development of their own small tractor. Much of the Research and Development work was actually undertaken by Harry Ferguson Research Ltd., of Coventry, a part of Harry Ferguson Ltd. which was not acquired by Massey Harris at the 1954 merger. The BMC Mini tractor was introduced in December 1965; the BMC Mini name being chosen as it was considered to have more publicity value than Nuffield in the wake of the launch of the BMC 'Mini' car in 1959. Designed as an agricultural tractor, its size and power made it more suited for Parks & Gardens use.

Below: A BMC Mini fitted with Lambourn cab demonstrating a single furrow plough somewhere in East Anglia in 1966.

Opposite Page: The BMC mini was ideal for parks and gardens use, and the three illustrations show (top to bottom) a sports field in South London being scarified, aerated using a Sisis scarifier, and with a sprayer attachment. Tractors found themselves in Council ownership and were often repainted yellow before delivery. The BMC Mini was also purchased by Butlins for use at their holiday camps.

Above: The BMC Mini was given a larger 25HP diesel engine in 1968. The Mini name was dropped at this time in favour of adding the model to the Nuffield range whereupon it became the 4/25. The occasion is the Smithfield Show. A petrol engined version was also available.

Left: The drivers view of the Nuffield 4/25.

Above: The 4/25 to Agricultural HPU specification.   Points to note are the full lighting set, vertical exhaust and number plates.

Below: The 4/25 ploughing with a two furrow mounted plough.

Above: The 4/25 ploughing.   The plough is a single furrow reversible by Salopian.

Below: Operating a Bomford tiller.   The same tractor is in use here as above.   Note the Mil loader and radiator guard which in this case was part of the loader assembly.

Top: Rural Warwickshire in 1968 is the setting for this demonstration shot of a 4/25 with Mil 'Mini' fore end loader and muck fork attachment. The demonstrator is Ron Kettle, who worked for Nuffield in the early 1960s, through the creation of BLMC, and into the 1980s when the Gainsborough operation ended.

Above and right: Two further working shots of the 4/25 using tillage implements. These were taken at a demonstration - the fact that the tractor is on the move can be ascertained by the blurred rear wheels.

Left: The BMC four cylinder engine as fitted to the 10/60 tractor. This engine continued in use in the 4/65 as seen below and with Simms Minimec fuel injection equipment developed 60HP @ 2000rpm. Being a Multi purpose engine it could also be found in Commercial Vehicle use, for which a six cylinder version was also built - the latter finding its way into but a few owner conversions of Nuffield tractors

Below: The number on the Bonnet indicates that this was one of a number of demonstration tractors used to launch the new 4/65 and 3/45 models to press and public prior to the models going on sale in June 1967.

Opposite page upper: The Nuffield 4/65 gained a reputation all of its own and not a good one at that.   Its unfortunate styling was one point, but worse than that were the large number of warranty claims experienced at the time.   This is a 1968 example featuring a silver band on which the "Nuffield" name was displayed.

Opposite page lower: The 3/45 seen here is a 1967 example with plain decals.   The 3/45 maintained the same output as its predecessor the 10/42 at 45HP.

Above and below: Steelfab of Cardiff used this Nuffield 4/65 tractor in the development of their Industrial loader.   It was eventually launched by Steelfab in late 1968 as their SF162/180 digger loader.   The loader featured a single lever operation of the spool valve and the oil reservoir was built into the offside support member.

Above: In anticipation of the 1972 legislation requiring all tractors sold for agricultural use in the UK to have roll-over protection this Nuffield 4/65 is fitted with a Winsam safety cab.   Winsam were to supply all cabs fitted in production to Nuffield tractors but following the BMC/Leyland merger other counsels prevailed.

Below: The 1968 Royal Show with a 4/65 attached to a Bamfords "Wizzler" mower.   The "Wizzler" mower was the latest in haymaking and grasscutting ideas with its four rotating drums doing the same work as a reciprocating cutter bar.   The author of this book had a hand in making some of the early "Wizzlers" in 1966-7.

Above: The Nuffield 4/65 this time with a Duncan safety cab supplied by Alexander Duncan of Aberdeen. These early safety cabs usually retained the original mudguards.

Left: The shape of things to come: The Nuffield 4/25 tractor saw the least changes in appearance once the post merger policy on tractors had been formulated. Only the paint scheme was changed to Blue and the model redesignated the 154.

Above: The light weight of the Leyland 154 made it ideal for equipping as a high clearance tractor for spraying. Not only the weight factor but the extra ground clearance obtained in this way ensured that the crop received the minimum of damage on passage of the equipment.

Below: The Leyland 154 on test in early 1969 with a buckrake. Oversize rear tyres are fitted with industrial tread pattern.

Above and Below: *It was originally expected that the Nuffield name would be retained for the revised tractor range introduced in 1969 but in view of the reputation of the previous models it was decided that a new colour scheme and the adoption of the Leyland name would help sales.   Nevertheless underneath the new tinwork finished in blue and silver were the same 4/65 and 3/45 tractors.   The 3/45 became the 344 and the 4/65 became the 384.   The Nuffield name was demoted to small lettering just above the model number.*

Above: For the launch of the new models at the 1969 Smithfield Show a sectioned 384 was prepared by apprentices at the Bathgate factory. It is seen here on the stand at Earl's Court.

Below: With engine power increased to 70BHP the Leyland (Nuffield) 384 tractor makes easy work of ploughing on ground adjacent to the factory in November 1969.

Above: The Leyland range was expanded in the 1970s.   The 253, introduced in December 1971,   used a Perkins 3 cylinder engine which was stressed in the sump to carry the weight of the whole tractor thus eliminating the sideframes.   This model was the equivalent of the popular MF135.

Below: 1973 saw further changes to the range with only the 154 remaining.   The new Leyland 285 featured a Leyland 6/98 six cylinder engines, and other new features were 'live' hydraulics, 2 speed PTO, wet brakes and hydraulic operation of clutch and brakes.

Above: The Leyland 384 tractor with Bray 4WD conversion.   This model was only produced for a year before replacement by the last Bray Four 70.

Below: The Leyland 485 was the first 4WD model to be assembled completely at Bathgate.

Above: The Leyland 270 was uprated to 72HP in 1975 to become the 272.   A cabless example is seen here, which could only be sold to export territories..

Below: This 272 shows the option for certain territories which allowed the cab to be reduced to a skeleton.

Opposite page: For the UK market cabs were compulsory and the upper illustration shows a 285 whilst the lower shows a 272. These illustrations show the "Q" cabs introduced in 1976 when the styling on the tractors was also altered with a silver bonnet stripe.

Above: The Leyland 262 with loader. In March 1978 the Leyland "Synchro" gearbox was introduced. Tractors so equipped had red stripes added to the silver bonnet surround and the word "Synchro" placed between "Leyland" and the model designation.

Below: The Leyland 462 was a 1978 introduction and used an Italian "Carriro" front axle.

Above: The Leyland 4100 was the top of the range 4WD version of the 2100 introduced in 1973.   The Leyland 6/98 engine was again used in this model.

Below: The 1978 472 also used an Italian "Carriro" front axle and was otherwise the same as the 272. The "Synchro" gearbox gave 9 forward and 3 reverse speeds.

Above: The 1980 Smithfield Show saw further changes including a new black and yellow colour scheme. The 235 became the 302, which was built in Turkey.   It is seen on ground maintenance duties.

Below: The 502 used the Perkins AD3.152 engine and replaced the 245.

Above: The 604 shared the same 62HP Leyland 4/98DT engine as the 602.   Other features included fully live hydraulics, independent PTO, wet disc brakes and QM cab.

Below: The 702 is seen with de-luxe explorer cab.   This tractor and its equivalent 4WD brother (inset) had 72HP Leyland 4/98NT engines.

Above: The 800 series shared the same turbocharged Leyland 4/98TT engine and the common factor between the 600, 700, and 800 series was the use of the same transmission layout.   The 802 with explorer cab is seen here taking grain from a Claas combine.

Below.   The 804 and 802 compared.

Next Page: "Made better by Marshall" was the slogan in the new Marshall sales literature once production at Gainsborough started.   The tractors had to pass an 86 point check before leaving the works. The 62 HP 602 with explorer cab is seen (top), and the 82HP 802 is seen (centre).   New in November 1984 was the 904 with a 4 cylinder turbocharged Leyland engine.   Engines continued to be bought from Leyland.   The 100 series also introduced in 1984 are not covered in this publication as only the engines came from Leyland; the final link with the 1948 Nuffield had been broken.   Production of tractors at Gainsborough ceased in November 1985.

Above: Bray Industries of Feltham carried out 4WD conversions of Nuffield tractors. The 10/60 was launched in April 1966 and around 100 units were built until the replacement version using the 4/65 came in June 1967. Around 130 units were produced (below).

Nuffield, Leyland & Marshall Tractors - Specifications.

Nuffield 1948-69

Model	Engine	Cyls	Rating	Fuel	Gearbox	Produced	Notes.
M4/M3	Morris ETA	4	33HP	TVO	5f. 1r.	1948-54	
PM4/PM3	Morris ETA	4	36HP	Petrol	5f. 1r.	1948-54	
DM4/DM3	Perkins L4(TA)	4	38HP	Diesel	5f. 1r.	1950-54	
DM4(BMC)	BMC0EA2	4	39HP	Diesel	5f. 1r.	1954-57	Also DM3 (vee fronts)
Universal 4	BMC	4	40HP	Diesel	5f. 1r.	1957-61	
Universal 3	BMC	3	28HP	Diesel	5f. 1r.	1957-61	
3/42	BMC	3	39HP	Diesel	5f. 1r.	1961-63	
4/60	BMC	4	55HP	Diesel	5f. 1r.	1961-63	
10/42	BMC	3	39HP	Diesel	10f. 2r.	1964-67	
10/60	BMC	4	60HP	Diesel	10f. 2r.	1964-67	
BMC Mini	BMC	4	20HP	Diesel	9f. 3r.	1965-68	Petrol engine option
3/42	BMC	3	45HP	Diesel	10f. 2r.	1967-69	
4/65	BMC	4	65HP	Diesel	10f. 2r.	1967-69	
4/25	BMC	4	25HP	Diesel	9f. 3r.	1968-69	Petrol engine option

Leyland 1969-81 - Marshall 1982-85

Model	Engine	Cyls	Rating	Fuel	Gearbox	Produced	Notes.
154	BMC	4	25HP	Diesel	9f. 3r.	1969-73	
344	BMC	3	55HP	Diesel	10f. 2r.	1969-73	
384	BMC	4	70HP	Diesel	10f. 2r.	1969-73	Also 4WD variant.
253	Perkins A3.152	3	47HP	Diesel	10f. 2r.	1971-73	
154	BMC	4	25HP	Diesel	9f. 3r	1973-79	
245	Perkins A3.152	3	47HP	Diesel	10f. 2r.	1973-75	
255	Leyland	3	55HP	Diesel	10f. 2r.	1973-75	
270	Leyland	4	70HP	Diesel	10f. 2r.	1973-75	
285/485	Leyland	6	85HP	Diesel	10f. 2r.*	1973-80	485 - 4 wheel drive
2100/4100	Leyland	6	100HP	Diesel	10f. 2r.*	1973-80	4100 - 3 wheel drive
235	Leyland	4	35HP	Diesel	9f. 3r.	1979-80	
262/462	Leyland	4	62HP	Diesel	9f. 3r.*	1975-80	462 - 4 wheel drive
272/472	Leyland	4	72HP	Diesel	9f. 3r.*	1975-80	472 - 4 wheel drive
282/482	Leyland	4	82HP	Diesel	9f. 3r.*	1975-80	482 - 4 wheel drive
302	Leyland	4	30HP	Diesel	9f. 3r.	1981-85	Marshall from 1982
502	Perkins A3.152	3	47HP	Diesel	9f. 3r.	1980-85	Marshall from 1982
602/604	Leyland	4	62HP	Diesel	9f. 3r.	1980-85	Marshall from 1982
702/704	Leyland	4	72HP	Diesel	9f. 3r.	1980-85	Marshall from 1982
802/804	Leyland	4	80HP	Diesel	9f. 3r.	1980-85	Marshall from 1982
904	Leyland	4	90HP	Diesel	9f. 3r.	1985	Gainsborough only.

* After March 1978 all tractors were available with synchro gearboxes which had 9 forward and 3 reverse gears. The previous gearbox fitted to all models except the 154 had 10 forward and 2 reverse gears.

Serial Numbers.

Nuffield M4, 4M & Universal Four TVO

Date		Ser. No.
1948		NT501
1949		NT540
1950		NT2597
1951		NT6433
1952		NT9527
1953		NT12007
1954		NT13868
1955		NT14929
1956	January	NT15470
1956	March	1NT15509
1957	Ceased	1NT15746

Nuffield DM4, 4DM & Universal Four Diesel Standard PTO

Date	Perkins Engine No.	Ser. No.
1950	35390	NT50001
1951	37999	NT50563
(Changed to 50,000)		
1952	52366	NT51915
1953	2058483	NT53303
1954	2066734	NT56130
(Last P4 engine No. 2070058)		
1954	BMC Engine.	DE1001
1955		DE3563
1956	January	DE9186
1956	March	DE10388
1957	January	DE14540
1958	August	4DM787-501
1959		4DM787-1857
1960	January	4DM787-7835
1961	December (Ceased)	4DM787-20558

Nuffield Universal Four Independent PTO

1957	August	DM4792-501
1958		DM4792-1080
1959		DM4792-2530
1960		DM4792-3436
1961	November (Ceased)	DM4792-11425

Nuffield 4/60 Standard and Independent PTO

1961	November	24000
1962		24554
1963		34598
1964	January	48290
1964	September (Ceased)	

Nuffield 10/60 Standard & De Luxe.

1964	October	60B 57420
1965	January	60B 62409
1966	January	60B 79421
1967	January	60B 93076
1967	June (Ceased)	60B 98880

Nuffield 4/65

1967	June	99001
1968		
1969	Ceased.	

Nuffield Universal Three (all models)

1957	August	3DL771-501
1958		3DL771-1546
1959		3DL771-3314
1960		3DL771-5759
1961	December (Ceased)	3DL771-8049

Nuffield 3/42

1961	November	24000
1962		24554
1963		34598
1964	September (Ceased)	48290
(in same series as 4/60)		

Nuffield 10/42 Standard PTO

1964	October	42B 57436
1965	January	42B 62393
1966	January	42B 79421
1967	January	42B 93076
1967	June (Ceased)	42B 98875

Nuffield 10/42 Deluxe, serials as above but with prefix 42N.

Nuffield 3/45

1967	June	
1968		
1969	November (Ceased)	

BMC Mini

1965	December	16D 101
1966	January	16D 441
1967	January	16D 2599
1967	June	16D 2671
1968	October (Ceased)	16D 4301

Nuffield 4/25

1968	November	25P 101
1969	December (Ceased)	

Bray Four 10/60

1966	April	0002 A
1967	January	0083 A
1967	June (Ceased)	0106 A

Bray Four 4/65

1967	June	7HN 0150 A
1968		8AN 0205 A
1969	Ceased	9AN 0287

Leyland 344

1969		344 135009
1972	Ceased	344 156144

Leyland 384

1969		384 135001
1972	Ceased	384 156144

Leyland 154

1969		154D 6301
1972		154D 16701

(petrol engined prefix 25P)

Thanks go to Jim Wilkie for providing most of the above data which is, we regret incomplete due to the records, in part being unobtainable.
If further information comes to light it will be published in "Vintage Tractor".